Electrical Circuits

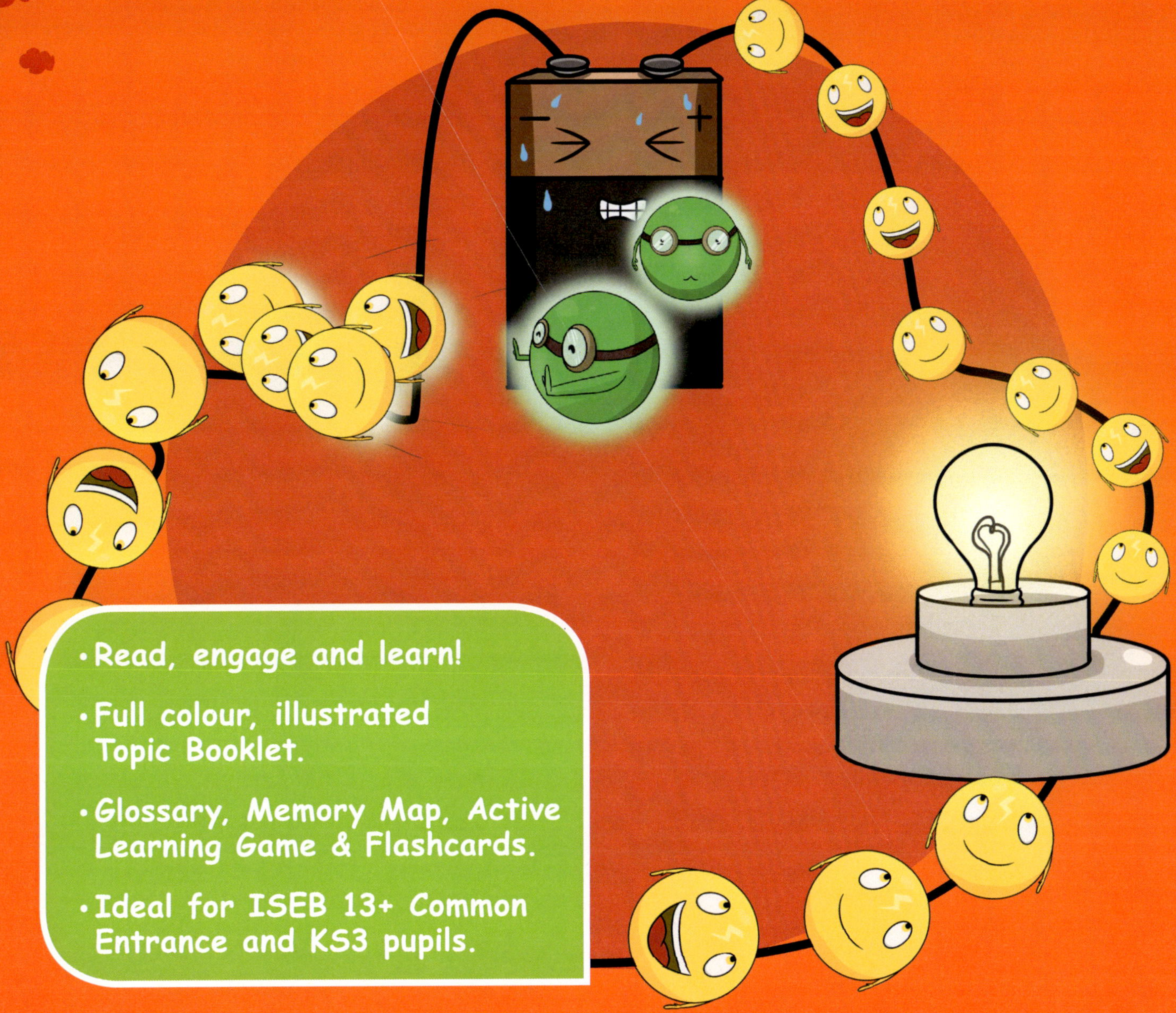

- Read, engage and learn!

- Full colour, illustrated Topic Booklet.

- Glossary, Memory Map, Active Learning Game & Flashcards.

- Ideal for ISEB 13+ Common Entrance and KS3 pupils.

This Oaka™ Books Topic Booklet goes hand in hand with the Active Learning Pack on this topic. The pack includes a Write Your Own Notes Booklet, an Active Learning Game and Question & Answer Flashcards.

Fresh Focus on Learning

Electrical Circuits Glossary

 **Ammeter:** Measures electric current (I).

 **Components:** The parts that make up an electrical circuit (e.g lamps, motors and switches).

 **Ampere (Amp):** The unit of current.

 **Connect:** To join together.

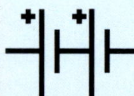 **Battery:** Stores chemical energy. Made of two or more electrical cells.

 **Current:** Movement of electric charge around a complete circuit.

 **Bulb (Lamp):** Transforms electrical energy into heat and light.

 **Electrical Cell:** Stores chemical energy. Two or more of these in series form a battery.

 **Buzzer:** Transforms electrical energy into sound energy.

 **Electrical Insulator:** Material that does not conduct electricity.

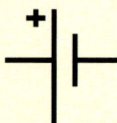 **Cell:** Stores chemical energy. Two or more of these in series form a battery.

 **Electricity:** A form of energy.

 **Charge:** Positive and negative charge. Electrons have a negative charge.

 **Energy:** Light, sound, thermal, kinetic, electrical and chemical are all forms of energy.

 **Chemical Energy:** Energy stored in food, fuels and electrical cells.

 **Fuse:** A thin metal wire that melts when the electric current gets too big.

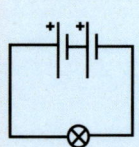 **Circuit:** Two or more electrical components connected together in an unbroken loop.

 **Hazard:** A danger.

Electrical Circuits Glossary

 **Insulator**: Material or substance that does not allow energy to move through it easily.

 **Resistance**: Makes it difficult for the electric current to flow.

 **Kinetic Energy**: Movement energy.

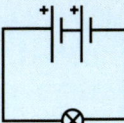 **Series Circuit**: An electric circuit with components placed one after the other.

 **Light Energy**: The form of energy that we can see.

 **Static Electricity**: Small charges that jump between materials.

 **Lamp (Bulb)**: Transforms electrical energy into heat and light.

 **Switch**: Used to make or break a complete circuit.

 **Metals**: Good conductors of electricity.

 **Symbol**: A simple diagram or letter.

 **Motor**: Transforms electrical energy into kinetic (movement) energy.

 **Transfer**: To move or change.

 **Negative**: One terminal of a battery. There are negative and positive terminals on batteries.

 Voltage: How much energy electrons in the circuits gain or lose across components.

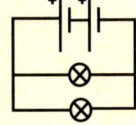 **Parallel Circuit**: Electrical circuits made with two or more loops. Each loop is a complete circuit.

 **Voltmeter**: Measures voltage (V).

 **Positive**: One terminal of a battery. There are negative and positive terminals on batteries.

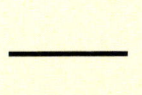 **Wire**: Used to connect electrical circuits. Made from metal (often copper).

Electrical Circuits

1 What is Electricity?

- Televisions, washing machines and torches all use **electrical energy**.

- This is a **series circuit**, showing how a torch is connected.

2 Electric Current

- **An electric current** must move through the wire to make the lamp glow.

- When we open the switch, the **lamp** goes out!

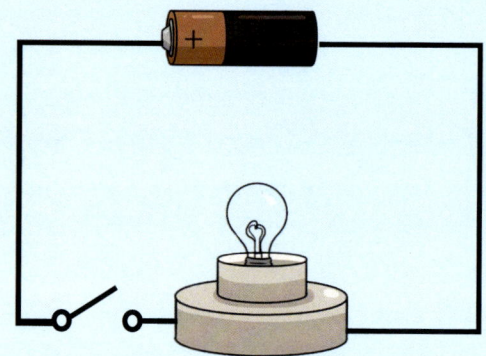

3 Types of Energy

Electricity is a form of energy.

Remember:

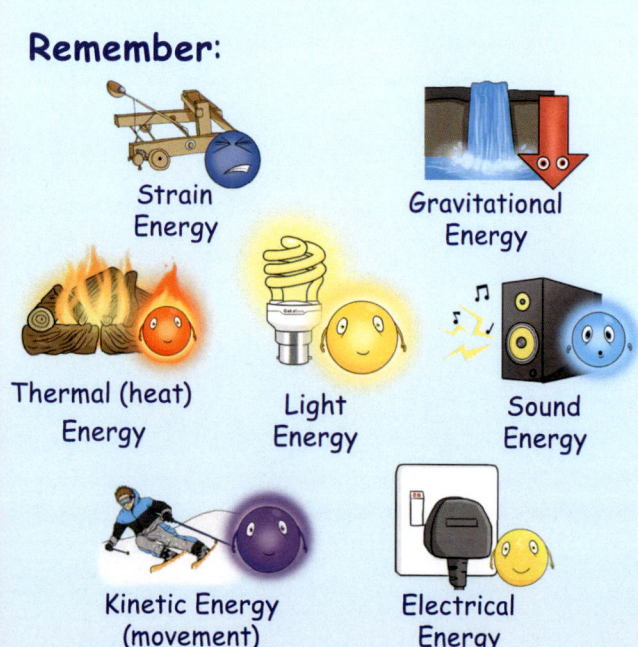

Strain Energy

Gravitational Energy

Thermal (heat) Energy

Light Energy

Sound Energy

Kinetic Energy (movement)

Electrical Energy

4 Stored Energy

- **Chemical energy** is stored in **food**, **fuels** and in **electrical cells**.

- A battery is made up of two or more **electrical cells** joined together.

Batteries contain **Chemical Energy**

Electrical Circuits

5   Conductors

- We use metal wires to **connect circuits**.

- Metals are good **conductors** of electricity. Electricity moves **through** conductors.

6   Insulators

- Some materials don't let electricity pass through them.

- These are **electrical insulators**.

- Plastic, rubber and wood are all good **electrical insulators**.

Electricity can't go through us!

7   Components

- The wires must be connected to **both** sides of **components**, like **lamps** and **motors**.

- The **electricity** goes through them.

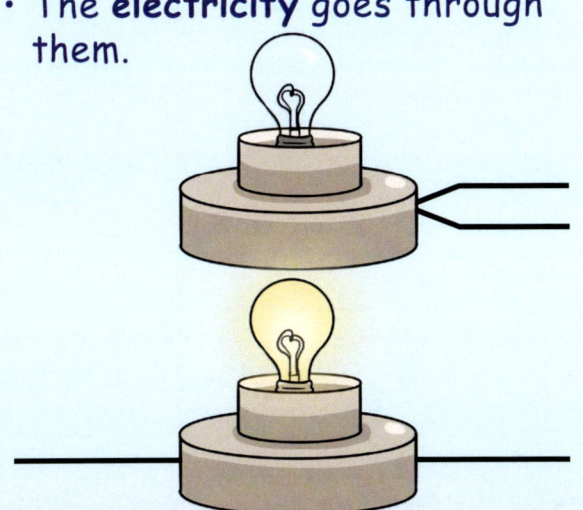

8   Light Energy

- A **lamp** changes **electrical energy** into **light (and thermal) energy** in a **circuit**.

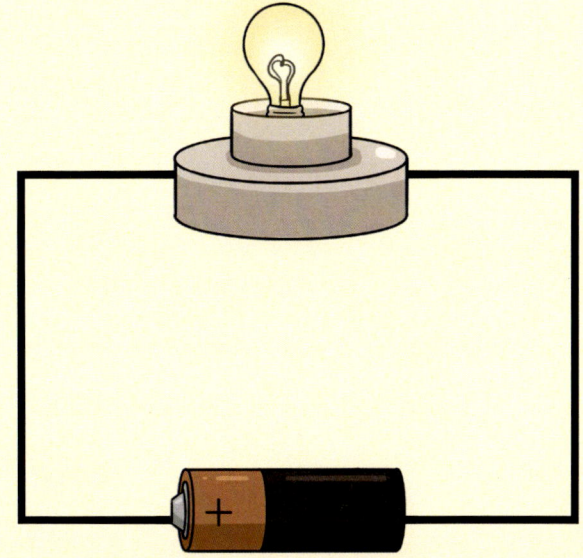

This booklet is not to be photocopied. Thank you.

2

Electrical Circuits

9   Kinetic Energy

- A **motor** changes **electrical energy** into **kinetic energy**.

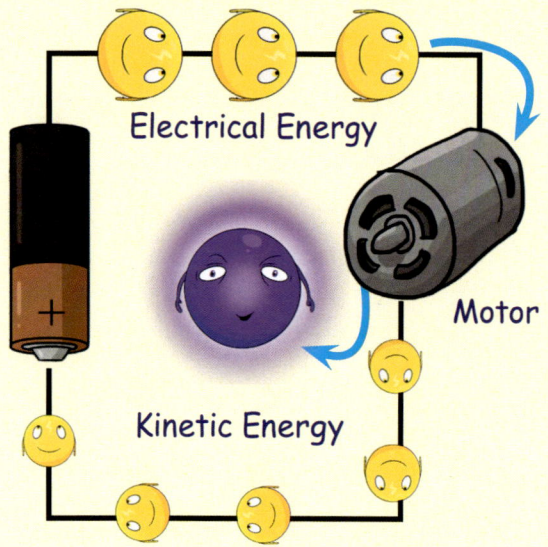

Electrical Energy

Motor

Kinetic Energy

10   Series Circuit

- In a **series circuit**, if one **lamp** breaks then **all** the **lamps** go out!

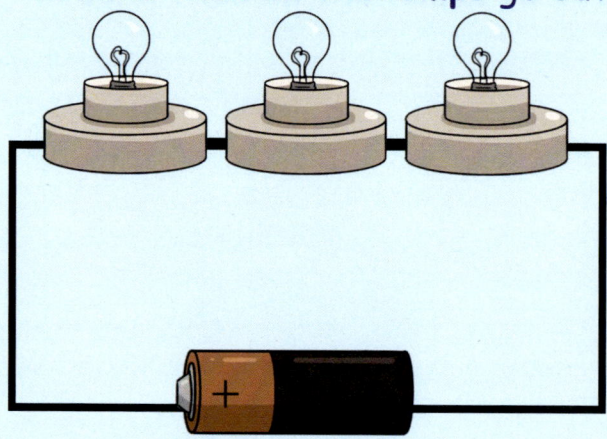

- The electricity **can't** go through all the lamps.
- The circuit is **broken**.

11   Current

- When tiny **electrical charges** move in the wire of a **circuit** it is called a **current**.

- For an **electric current** to move we need a complete **circuit**.

- We also need something to push the **current** round.

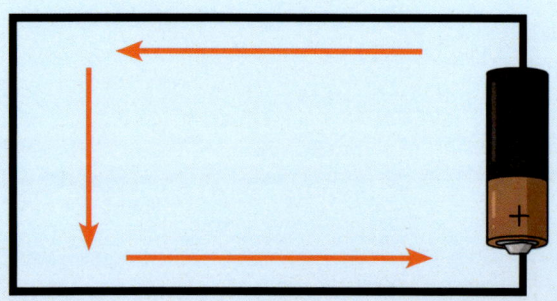

12   Electrons

- The **chemical energy** in a **battery** pushes these tiny **electrical charges** round the **circuit**.

- The tiny **charges** in the wires are called **electrons**.

Electrical Circuits

13 Ammeter

- The **ammeter** measures current.

- It tells us how many **charges** are moving through a **circuit**.

- **Current** is measured in **amperes** (Amps for short)

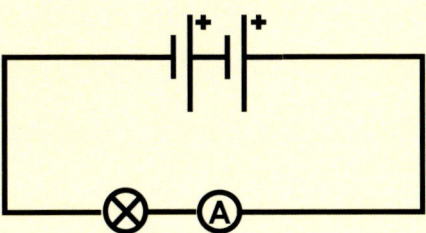

- Connect the positive terminal on the battery to the positive terminal on the Ammeter.

14 Losing Energy
(Not tested for CE)

Voltage tells us how much **energy** the **electrons** in the wire gain or lose **across** a component.

- Electrons **gain** energy across **batteries**.

- Electrons **lose** energy across **components** like **lamps** and **motors**.

Energy Before   Energy After

15 Voltage
(Not tested for CE)

- The **voltage** in a circuit is measured using a **voltmeter**.

- The **voltage** tells us how much **energy** the electrons have **before and after** a component.

- **Voltage** is measured in **volts**. We use the **symbol V.**

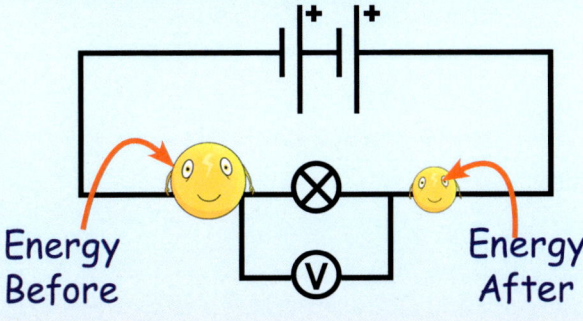

Energy Before   Energy After

16 Resistance

- **Resistance** tells us how hard it is for **electrons** to move **through** components in a circuit.

- When **electrons** move through **components** with high **resistance**, like **lamps**, they lose a lot of their **energy**.

Resistance is measured in Ohms (Ω). We use the **symbol R.**

Electrical Circuits

17 Changing Energy

- When electrons move **through** a lamp some of their energy is lost as **light energy** and **thermal energy**.

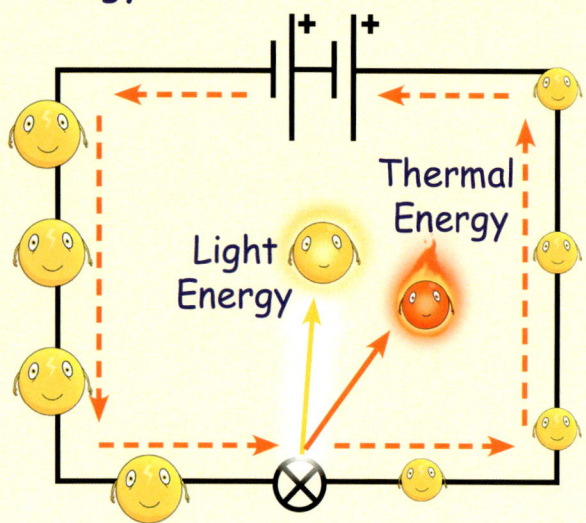

18 Work It Out!
(Not tested for CE)

- We can use equations to calculate **voltage**, **current** and **resistance**.

- **Voltage = Current X Resistance**

- If we know that the **Current** is 4, and the **Resistance** is 2, then

- **Voltage = Current X Resistance**

- **Voltage = 4 X 2**

- **Voltage = 8V**

19 Use a Triangle
(Not tested for CE)

- There are three equations, one to work out **voltage**, one for **current** and one for **resistance**.

- We can use a **triangle** to remember them.

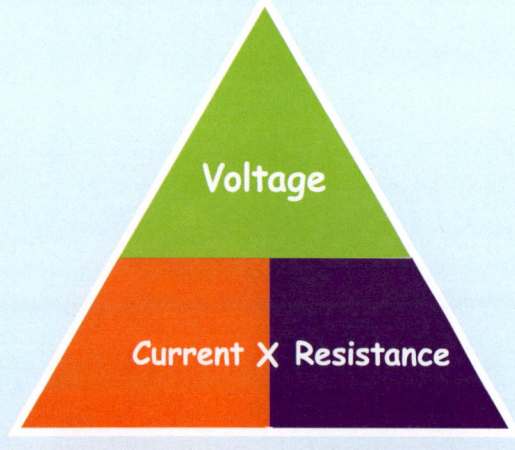

20 Voltage
(Not tested for CE)

- Cover the value we want to calculate.

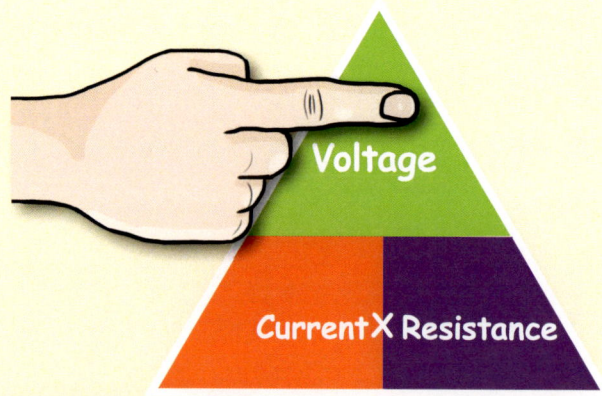

Voltage = Current X Resistance

Electrical Circuits

21 — Current
(Not tested for CE)

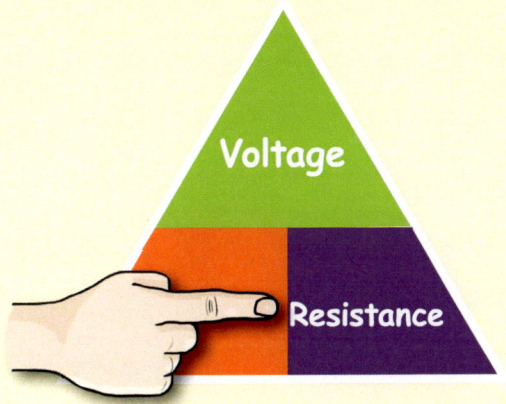

Current = Voltage / Resistance

22 — Resistance
(Not tested for CE)

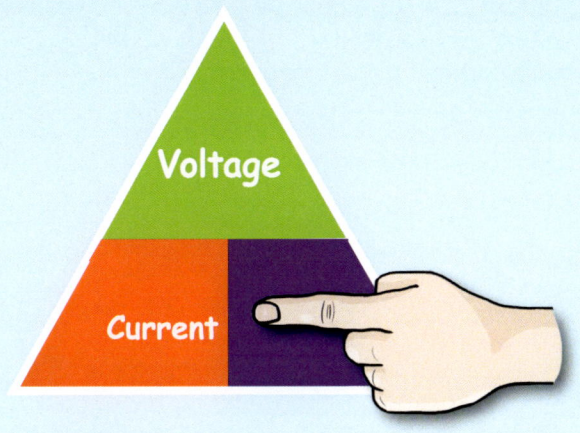

Resistance = Voltage / Current

23 — Let's recap...

A **circuit** must be complete with no breaks.

The **chemical energy** in a **battery** pushes the charges (**electrons**) round the **circuit**.

24 — Let's recap...

Voltage tells us how much **energy** the **electrons** in the wire gain or lose across a **component**.

- The **movement** of **electrons** through the **circuit** is called an **electric current**.

Components with high **resistance**, **slow** the flow of **current**.

Electrical Circuits

25 Transforming Energy

- The **electrical energy**, in the **circuit** can be changed (**transformed**) to **light energy**, **thermal energy** and **kinetic energy** by **components**.

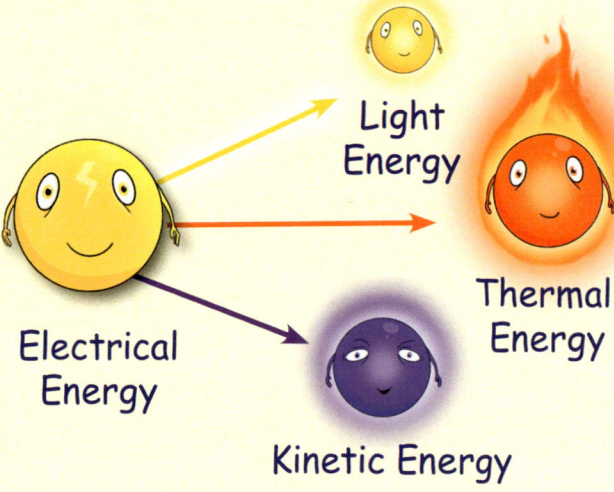

Electrical Energy

Light Energy

Thermal Energy

Kinetic Energy

26 Definition: Voltage

You need to know these definitions:

Voltage (V) tells us how much energy the electrons, in the wire, gain or lose across a component.

5.0V

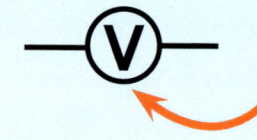

A voltmeter tells us how much voltage there is.

27 Definition: Current

When **electrons** move round the wire of a **circuit** it is called a **current** (I).

28 Definition: Resistance

Resistance (R) is a measure of how hard it is for **electrons** to move through **components** in a **circuit**.

- **Resistors** cause a lot of **resistance**.

Electrical Circuits

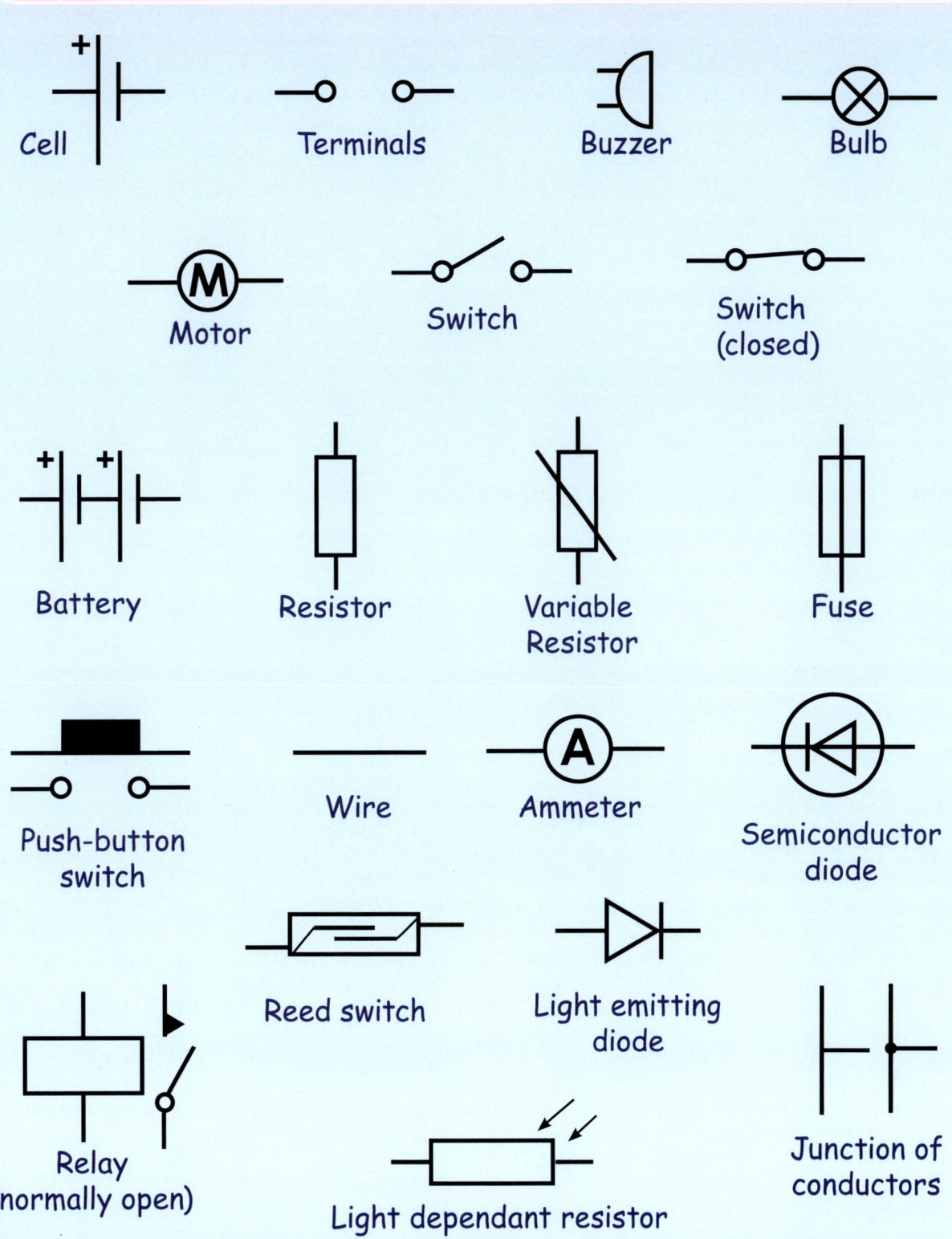

Cell

Terminals

Buzzer

Bulb

Motor

Switch

Switch (closed)

Battery

Resistor

Variable Resistor

Fuse

Push-button switch

Wire

Ammeter

Semiconductor diode

Reed switch

Light emitting diode

Relay (normally open)

Light dependant resistor

Junction of conductors

Electrical Circuits

29   The Wire

- Wires are made of metal, they are full of the tiny **charges** that we call **electrons**.

- The **electrons** are there all the time. They do **not** get used up.

- Batteries give **electrons energy** and push them round the wires in a circuit.

30   The Cell

- The **cell** stores **chemical energy**.

- The **chemical energy** is used to push **electrons** through the **circuit**.

- The **cell** has a **positive** terminal and a **negative** terminal.

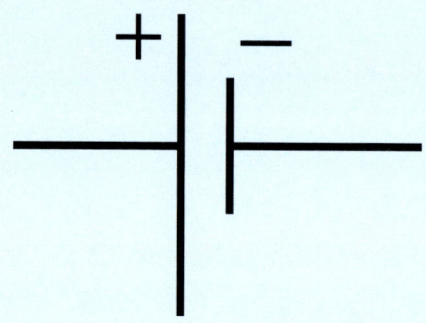

31   Batteries

- **Batteries** are made from more than one **cell** joined together.

- **Cells** and **batteries** only push in **one direction**. When you join them together, they must always point in the **same direction**.

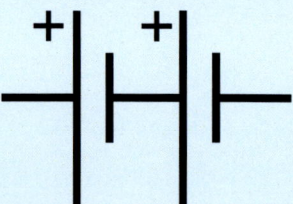

- The **positive** end of one **battery** connects to the negative end of the next **battery**.

32   Switches

- If the switch is **open**, the battery **cannot** push electrons round the circuit.

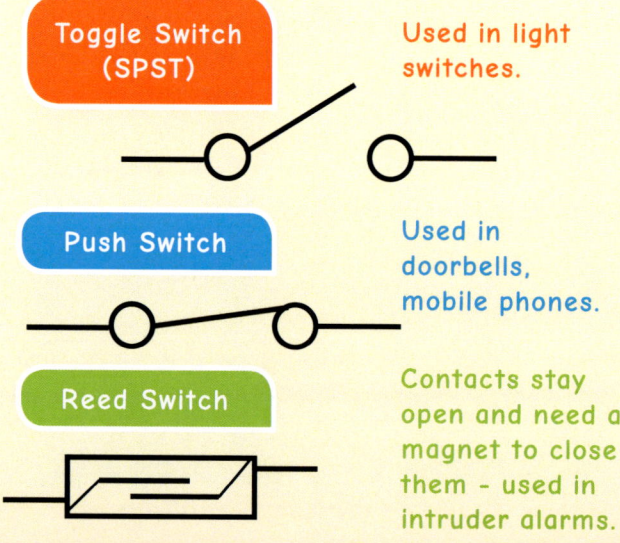

Toggle Switch (SPST) — Used in light switches.

Push Switch — Used in doorbells, mobile phones.

Reed Switch — Contacts stay open and need a magnet to close them - used in intruder alarms.

Electrical Circuits

33   Lamps (Bulbs)

- **Lamps** have high **resistance**.

- It is hard for the battery to push **electrons** through the lamp.

- As the **electrons** are pushed through, lots of **energy** is **transformed** to **light** and **heat energy**.

Thermal Energy

Light Energy

34   Motors

- As **electrical energy** moves through a **motor**, it is transformed to **kinetic energy** (**movement energy**).

- **Batteries** only push **electrons** in one direction.

- If you swap the terminals on the battery, the **motor** will spin the other way!

35   Resistors

- **Resistors** make it hard for **batteries** to push **electrons** round the circuit.

- The **higher** the **resistance**, the **smaller** the current.

- Remember: **current** is **electrons** being pushed around a **circuit**.

No Resistance

LARGE CURRENT

Smaller Current

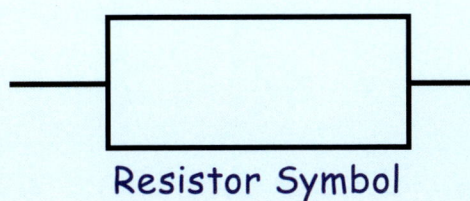

Resistor Symbol

Very Small Current

Electrical Circuits

36   Variable Resistors

- With some **resistors** we can change their **resistance**. These are called **variable resistors**.

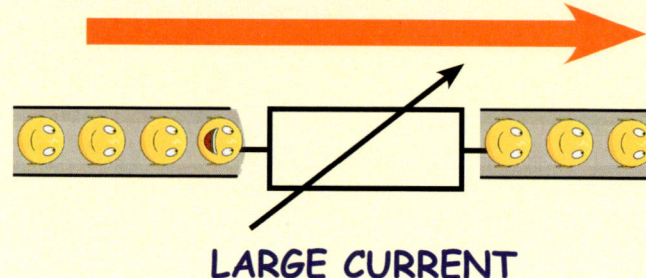

LARGE CURRENT

Big Resistance = Small Current

Small Resistance = Big Current

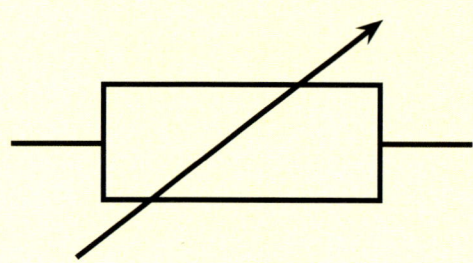

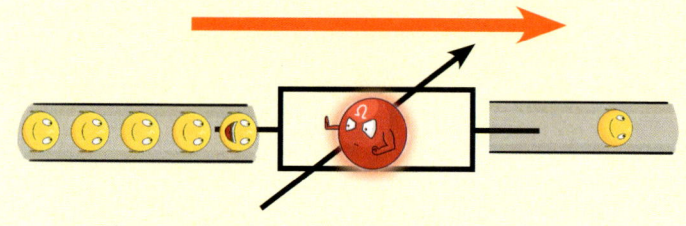

More Resistance = Smaller Current

37   Circuits in Action

- This is a **series circuit**. All the **components** are in a single loop.

- The **battery** uses its **chemical energy** to push **electrons** round the **circuit**.

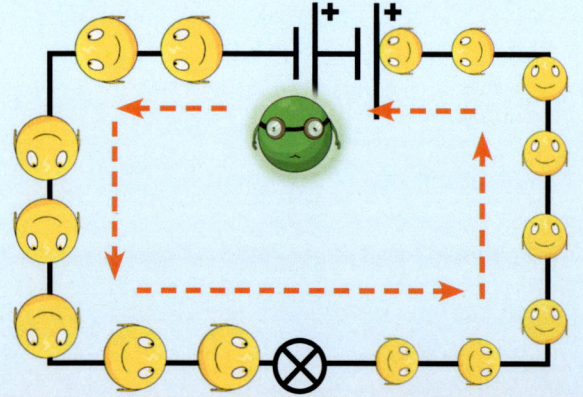

38   Circuits in Action

- The **wires** link the **circuit**.

- **Electrons** in the **wire** are pushed by the **battery**.

- The **lamp** transforms **electrical energy** to **light** and **thermal energy**.

Get moving!

Electrical Circuits

39 Switches

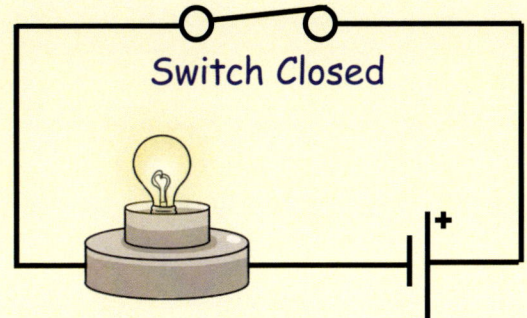

Switch Closed

When the **switch** is closed, the **lamp** lights up straight away!

Don't Forget!

- The **wire** is full of **electrons**. The **electrons** don't come from the **battery**. They are in the wire. The **battery** just pushes them.

40 More Voltage

- More **batteries** = more push
- More push = higher **voltage**
- Higher **voltage** = more **energy**
- More **energy** = brighter **lamp**!

41 Transformation

Lamps transfer **electrical energy**

to **light** and **thermal energy**.

- If you put more **lamps** into a series circuit, the **electrical energy** is shared out between them.

- There is less **energy** for each **lamp**.

- The **lamps** are dimmer.

42   Voltage in Circuits

- We measure the **voltage** in a circuit using a **voltmeter**.

- Remember: **voltage** tells us how much **energy** the **electrons**, in the wire gain or lose across a **component**.

- Two **lamps** in a **series circuit** have to **share** the **voltage**.

- The **battery** has to push **electrons** through both.

- This is twice as hard as pushing **electrons** through one **lamp**.

I've got to work twice as hard with two lamps to light!

43   Voltage in Circuits

- The **voltmeter** tells us how much **energy** the **electrons** have **gained** from the **battery**. (9.0 Volts in the diagram).

- The **Voltmeter (by the lamps)** tell us how much **energy** the **electrons lose** at each **lamp** (4.5 Volts).

44   Flat Battery

- The **battery** pushes the **electrons** until all of its **chemical energy** has been **changed** to **light & thermal energy** at the **lamps**.

Don't forget:

- **Voltmeters** must be connected to each side of a **component**.

- The **voltmeter** is connected 'in parallel'.

Electrical Circuits

45   Current in Circuits

- We measure the **current** in a circuit using an **ammeter**.

- The **current** is the **same** at all points in a **series circuit**.

- The **current** (the moving **electrons**) is **not** used up.

- **Energy** from the moving **electrons** is changed to thermal and light energy.

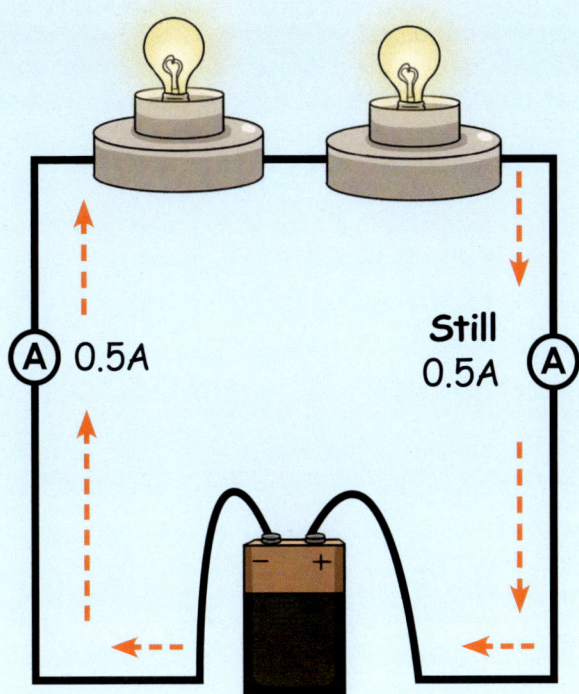

A 0.5A   Still 0.5A A

46   Resistance in Circuits
(Not tested in CE)

- Remember: **resistance** is how hard it is for **electrons** to move through **components** in a **circuit**.

- We can **calculate** the **resistance** of each **lamp** using the triangle.

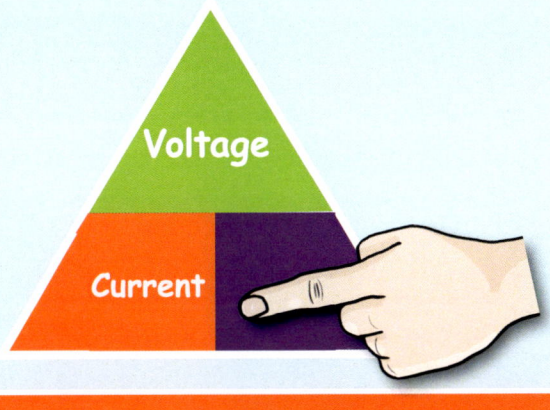

Voltage

Current

47   Resistance in Circuits

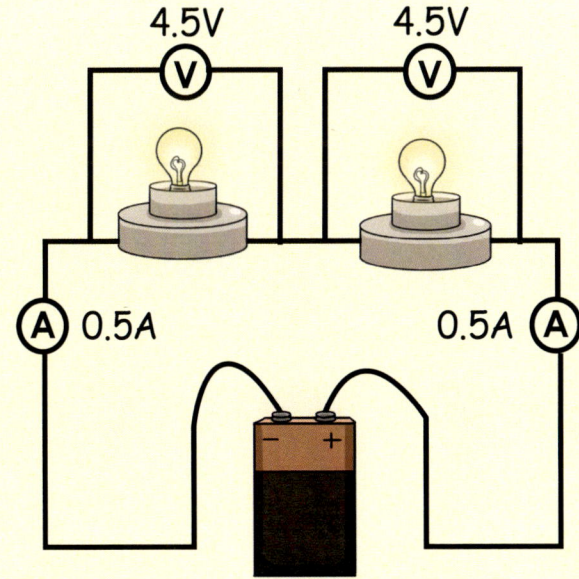

4.5V   4.5V

A 0.5A   0.5A A

- Resistance = Voltage / Current
- Resistance = 4.5 / 0.5
- Resistance = 9 Ω

Electrical Circuits

48 Parallel Circuits

- **Parallel circuits** are made up of **two** or more loops.

- Each loop is a complete **circuit**.

- Each **circuit** can work on its own.

- The **current** is divided up between each **circuit**.

- Both **lamps** in this **circuit** are bright.

- Set up this **circuit** and measure the **voltage** across each **lamp**!

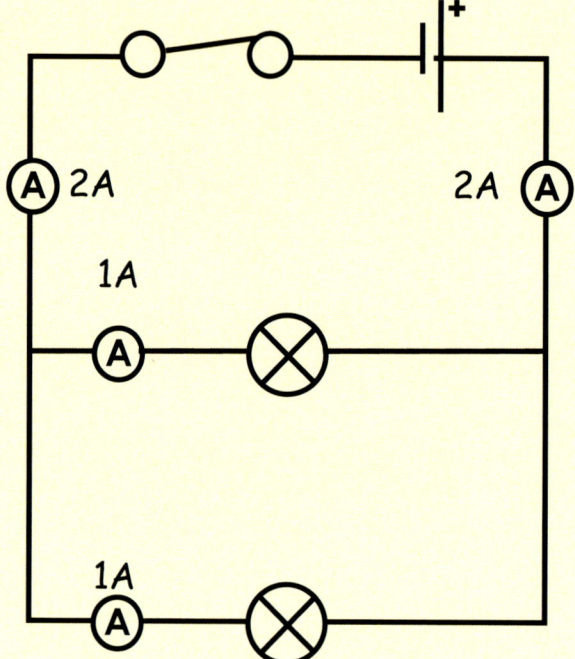

49 Parallel Circuits

- If there are 2 or more lamps in one circuit, they will all go out if one breaks.

- If a lamp breaks all the **current** flows through the other circuit so the lamp stays on.

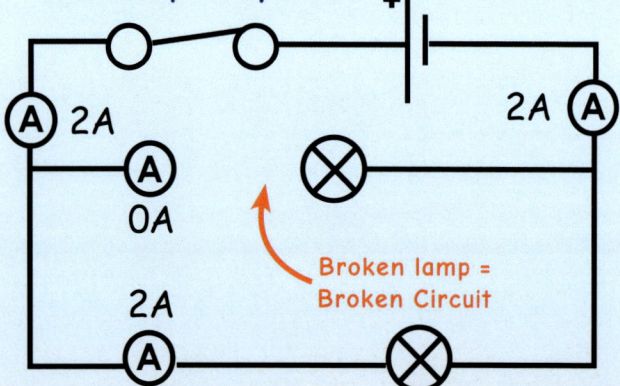

Broken lamp = Broken Circuit

- **Parallel circuits** are used in Christmas tree lights. If one **lamp** goes out, the others stay on.

- **Parallel circuits** are used in houses.

- The **components** in each loop get the same **voltage** (push) from the **battery**.

Electrical Circuits

50   Short Circuits

- Electricity takes the easiest route in a circuit.

- A short circuit happens when the current flows round the circuit but does not go through any components.

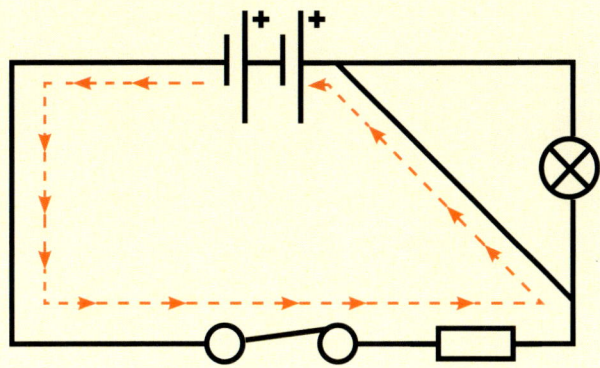

51   Fuses

- **Fuses** protect us. They stop appliances getting damaged if too much **current** flows through them.

- Inside a **fuse** there is a piece of **wire.**

- If the **current** gets too high, the wire gets hot and melts. The **circuit** is broken.

- We say the **fuse** has blown!

52   Fuses

- Different types of **fuses** can carry different amounts of **current** (Amps).

- Common **fuse** ratings are: 1A, 3A, 5A and 13A.

- The **fuse** rating should be higher than the **current** in a circuit.

- A **circuit** that has 10A flowing through it should use a 13A **fuse**.

53   Danger!

- A short circuit means too much current will flow.

- It can make a battery or appliance hot.

- It can cause electrical fires.

About Oaka Books

Children learn best when they are engaged...

Our aim is to help children enjoy learning by making it fun! That way they will succeed.

Following Common Entrance ISEB 13+ and National Curriculum guidelines for KS3.

Design and layout of our books follow guidelines from the British Dyslexia Association.

Three Easy Steps

Read: the easy to follow bullet point Topic Booklet.

Engage: Play the Active Learning Game.

Learn: When you understand the topic, test yourself using the Write Your Own Notes Book. You can use the Topic Booklet to help if you get stuck.

One (short) Topic at a time:

For some students, a big book is a big turn off. That's why we focus on one topic at a time. Short and to the point.

Reading Age

This booklet is suitable for children with a reading age of 10 ½ years.

Topic Packs for KS1, KS2 & KS3 Include:

History
Geography
Chemistry
Biology
Physics

Please visit www.oakabooks.co.uk for more information about forthcoming titles

© Copyright 2017 Oaka Books. All rights reserved.
Written by Stuart Lawes, BSc, PGCE. Illustrations by Laurence Andrew Page.

First paperback edition printed 2014 in the United Kingdom.
A catalogue record for this book is available from the British Library.

ISBN 978-1-909892-51-4
No part of this book shall be reproduced or transmitted in any form or by any means, electronic or mechanical, including photocopying, recording or by any information retrieval system without written permission of the copyright owner or a licence permitting restricted copying issued by the Copyright Licensing Agency Ltd, Saffron House, 6-10 Kirby Street, London EC1N 8TS Tel: 020 7400 3100   Fax: 020 7400 3101   Email: cla@cla.co.uk   Web: www.cla.co.uk

Designed, set and published by Oaka™ Books.

To order other titles from Oaka™ Books, please email info@oakabooks.co.uk or visit www.oakabooks.co.uk, or phone: +44 (0) 2392 388519.

Acknowledgements
Our huge thanks go to the many teachers who have been involved in the development of this series of learning guides. Special thanks to Joy Gardiner, for producing hundreds of illustrations, to Kate Doehren, for her enthusiasm and invaluable assistance to my wonderful daughter Sophie, for being the inspiration for the books and, of course, to Charlie, for believing in them.

ISBN 978-1-909892-51-4

CE/KS3
Electrical Circuits

Topic Booklet

ISBN 978-1-909892-51-4
9 781909 892514

Produced in association with Kate Doehren, MA Ed, B.Ed Hons, RSA Dip, Sp LD/Dyslexia
Head of Learning Support, Hurstpierpoint College
© Copyright Oaka™ Books 2017